HOW PLEASANT TO KNOW MR. LEAR!

An Icon Original

LONDON

Published in the Icon Series July 1964

Cover design by Nicholas Fisk

Icon Books are published by Icon Books Ltd., 9 Down Street, Mayfair, London, W.1, and are made and printed in Great Britain by Love and Malcomson Ltd, Redhill, Surrey.

Margaret Rutherford Says

"HOW PLEASANT TO KNOW Mr. LEAR!"

A selection from the works of
Edward Lear
made by
MARGARET RUTHERFORD

With an introduction by Frank Baker

ICON BOOKS LIMITED

CONTENTS

SELF-PORTRAIT OF
THE LAUREATE OF NONSENSE

How pleasant to know Mr. Lear!
  Who has written such volumes of stuff!
Some think him ill-tempered and queer,
  But a few think him pleasant enough.

His mind is concrete and fastidious,
  His nose is remarkably big;
His visage is more or less hideous,
  His beard it resembles a wig.

He has ears, and two eyes, and ten fingers,
  Leastways if you reckon two thumbs;
Long ago he was one of the singers,
  But now he is one of the dumbs.

He sits in a beautiful parlour,
  With hundreds of books on the wall;
He drinks a great deal of Marsala,
  But never gets tipsy at all.

He has many friends, laymen and clerical;
  Old Foss is the name of his cat;
His body is perfectly spherical,
  He weareth a runcible hat.

When he walks in a waterproof white,
  The children run after him so !
Calling out, 'He's come out in his night-
  Gown, that crazy old Englishman, oh !'

He weeps by the side of the ocean,
  He weeps on the top of the hill ;
He purchases pancakes and lotion,
  And chocolate shrimps from the mill.

He reads but he cannot speak Spanish,
  He cannot abide ginger-beer :
Ere the days of his pilgrimage vanish,
  How pleasant to know Mr. Lear !

EDWARD LEAR

INTRODUCTION

How pleasant to know Mr. Lear ...

Of all the many sentences with which one might begin an introduction to a new collection of his meloobious verse, these six simple words surely make the best—and 'meloobious', I must at once make clear to those who now come to Mr. Lear for the first time, is no printer's error. If it had been I imagine he would have left it. In fact, it is Lear language.

And, of course, he wrote the line—of himself : the first line of one of his most engaging poems, written 'by way of preface' to *A Book of Nonsense,* verses and drawings he made for the 'great-grandchildren, grand-nephews, and grand-nieces of Edward, the 13th Earl of Derby', published and dedicated to them many years after he had ceased to be tutor in the Earl's household.

Many there must be who, knowing nothing of this large, lone, rather unhappy man, have none the less heard of the Runcible Spoon. We may well say that we do not know what a Runcible Spoon is. Is it a kind of ladle attached to the lasket of the vessel in which the Owl and the Pussy-cat (Mr. Foss, I hope) sailed away to the Land where the Bong-tree grows? Idle to ask such questions, which other students of Lear have also asked; because we are specifically told what the Spoon was. It was Runcible.

Could we at these times catch the poet and the artist whose pages make up this book, would we still find him at San Remo in that second villa he had built exactly similar to the first, in order not to disturb his dearly cherished cat, Mr. Foss—if not, indeed, in a third or thirty-third villa, assuming that more large hotels had got in the way of his view of the sea, (which is why he had built the second)?* Would we find him there, over a glass of Marsala, musing on his many years of travel? Looking back on his years of experience from the days of his birth into a struggling family of many many sisters in London North Seven and, in the words of a poet he greatly and rightly loved, seeing them as the structure of an 'arch'

> *... wherethro'*
> *Gleams that untravell'd world whose margin fades*
> *For ever and for ever when I move ... ?*

Not improbable. And he would, I think, be composing verses in a grave Tennysonian mood, a mood of reflection, musing on his wandering life and seeing life itself as an unfinished chapter of nonsense which transcends sense (if that can be done); a nonsense which, in the sublime definition of Sir Edward Strachey, Baronet, can only be explained when we do not ask what it is.

No. Not improbable. There, remembering that 'many a mad magenta minute lights the lavender of life,' he might still be ...

It is probably expected of me that I should give a brief biography of this lovable man, though others, especially Mr. Angus Davidson, have been of better service to him here. I shall skip through this in the hope that the rope I have flung at my feet will not coil up and hang me.

Edward—from Jeremiah Lear, stockbroker, and Ann Skerrit, daughter of a Durham sea-captain—one of twenty-

---

*Of his second villa Mr. Lear said: Nothing now could interrupt his light unless the fishes built.

one children—brother to thirteen sisters—prone to epilepsy, bronchitis and asthma—with a horror of horses, a terror of dogs, a dread of sea and ships—linguist who spoke and wrote in seven languages including Greek and Albanian—commercial artist at fifteen—myopic, bearded, obsessed with the prolongation of many noses—tutor to little people at Knowsley Hall—specialist student of the genus *psittacidae*—art-master to Queen Victoria at thirty-four—traveller in Sicily, Greece, Calabria, the Abruzzi, Albania, Corsica, the Ionian Islands, the Desert of Sinai, Lower Egypt, India, Corfu, Malta, Rome—who did not apply the word 'Limerick' to that form of verse he made so peculiarly and printably his own and who was not born on the Highgate Heights—died, attended, it is hoped by Giorgio Kokali, his devoted Albanian servant, in San Remo in 1888.

He did not anticipate the renown that his nonsense verses and his drawings slowly brought to him. But he protested firmly in a railway carriage from London to Guildford when an unknown elderly gentleman told two unknown ladies with two unknown little boys who had lauded *A Book of Nonsense* that it had really been composed by the Earl of Derby, 'Earl' being an anagram from 'Lear'. Not unlike another Master, Sullivan, who yearned after grand opera and achieved grander operetta, he pined for the large canvas, the oils and the brushes. And although his smaller water-colours have a lucidity and sense of space which we soon recognize as his, the oils, styled somewhat in the manner of the pre-Raphaelites, do not throw open the gates to that unique world of art he discovered in the composition of the verses and drawings that all children of all ages have adored. These are as fresh and fabulous to-day as they were yesterday; and to-morrow will continue to guard them jealously from the impious. Even while I was writing this introduction my son Llewellyn came into my study, his mind on a mural scheme he has in view. He and his brother and sister remember Lear well from the happy days when I read him aloud and very much aloud (how many parents

11

have cause to be grateful to Lear?) to summon them to sleep and dreams. I asked Llewellyn to come to my aid in the task I had undertaken, and refresh my ears again with the cry of the Dong; and out came the mysterious, moving, infinitely pathetic and strangely noble stanzas—out they came, ringing through the room in tones which I will declare would have moved old Lear himself.

> *When awful darkness and silence reigns*
> *Over the great Gromboolian plains . . .*

Who was his Jumbly Girl, who was she? 'With her sky-blue hands and her sea-green hair' did she call back comfort to his mind in the shape of that beloved sister Ann, who had early become a second mother to him? Whoever she symbolised—if she has to symbolise anyone—Lear never held her in reality. The few women to whom his affectionate and generous nature reached out soon faded from his scene. After the restless fever of the years of travel, years of innumerable sketches, drawings and paintings and letters, all thrown out with impeccable conscientiousness yet with a kind of innate self-distrust, he turned more and more in upon himself yet never away from the few close friends, most of them younger, whom he knew he could trust. At the Villa Tennyson he painted, painted, and he painted. Henry Strachey well describes the busy stage of his determined efforts, in a letter to his father :

His studio (was) a large room upstairs. He was then at work on a series of water-colours, and his method seemed to be to dip a brush into a large wide-necked bottle of water-colour, and when he had made one or two touches on the drawing, to carry it to the end of the room and put it on the floor, the performance being repeated till quite a row was arranged across the room.

One can almost feel the hesitation with which Lear applied his water-colours to the paper, when one looks at the results, and sees delicate pictures of such clarity and sparseness one almost begins to wish for the human figure of Mr. Lear, however small a blob, to appear. But he does not. Henry Strachey's description of the lonely artist is touching, as well as being funny:

Mr. Lear felt keenly the neglect of the world for his pictures, but he seemed anxious to prevent all but his nearest friends seeing them. When I was staying with him, it happened to be the afternoon on which he was supposed to be at home to show his pictures to possible buyers. Early in the afternoon he told me that he had sent his servants out, and was going to open the door himself. He explained that if anyone came he did not like he could send them away . . . as the afternoon advanced a ring at the door-bell was heard, and Mr. Lear went to open the door . . . I heard the voice of a lady inquiring if she could see the pictures, and I could hear Mr. Lear, in a voice of the most melancholy kind, telling her that he never showed his pictures now, he was much too ill; and from his voice and words I have no doubt the lady went away with the idea that a most unhappy man lived there. Mr. Lear came back to the gallery with much satisfaction at the working of his plan, which was so far superior to the servants' "not at home", as by his method he could send away bores and let in people he liked. Later on, some friends he wanted to see came, and the melancholy old man, too ill to show his pictures, changed into the most genial host. In the evenings he often sang; the *Yonghy Bonghy Bò* was inimitable. . . .

If, happily, the performance of the *Yonghy Bonghy Bò* was inimitable, it is unfortunate that the highly original style of his verse has not been so lucky—rather, truer to say, the verse is indeed inimitable, but many lesser versifiers, inebriated by the fertility of his imagination yet ignoring its purity, have dared to snatch some leaves from the laureate crown. In the case of his drawings we may note that Thurber bears a remarkable likeness to him, and this is more pleasing than distressing. But as to his verse, too many second-raters have copied Lear and survive now only as crushed and crinkled leaves, like those we find pressed between the pages of some musty old diary. Only one distinguished name, that of the Reverend Charles Lutwidge Dodgson (Lewis Carroll) can be accepted as to come into serious rivalry with him; and Carroll's world is, however strange and amazing, never so warm, so *homely,* as Lear's. I do not think that the Jumblies in their manifold travels ever had to come into contact with a Jabberwock—though, if they had, they would have exhibited the courage of their progenitor and faced the terrible beast with valour and distinction. Of the many puerile imitators, base people, who presumed to wallow and guzzle in Learland, treating words as hens treat eggs and never caring, the less said or heard of them the better.

There have been, of course, a select handful of versifiers whose labours in Lear's exotic country were not wasted, whose finished lines were not tinged by the smoke from the spirit lamp. For example, Sandys Wason, whose memorable comment on the varying shades of life I have quoted in this note. And in particular, another, who came near to the true emancipated joy of the *Timballo,* who at once saw the significance in a '*useful* cart,' who knew what it was to 'whistle and warble a moony song to the echoing sound of a coppery gong,' and had certainly spent solitary and possibly neurotic hours on the vast emptiness of the Great Gromboolian Plain. This is Constance Hargreaves. Her one slight collection of verse shows clearly that she had known what it was to languish *in terra deserta* while relishing to the full the exuberance of simple human delights. *Wayside Bundle,* printed very privately in commemoration of her old friend the Reverend Philip Archer, Master of Arts, many years ago, does yield here and there (and I mean here and there) fruit almost ripe enough to have fallen from the indigenous Lear tree. It is worth quoting from a curious poem in six quatrains, entitled 'The Unwilling Suitor' :

> *Oh, bring me the flute and the alto-bassoon,*
> *The mustard, the cress, and the water;*
> *The high and the diddle; the fiddle; for soon*
> *Must I go to make love to your daughter.*

In the same poem we have a hint that the poetess, who still lives to-day in strict yet reluctant retirement, possibly had personal contact of some kind with Lear in her very earliest days.

> *My life was complete before Agatha came;*
> *The rosemary, dapple and fawn;*
> *The carroway petal, the holloway flame,*
> *The gingham, the gallows, the dawn.*

It would be ridiculously presumptuous to read any meaning into the wholly subjective first line but surely it is not impermissible to assume from the third line that Constance and Edward had found common playing ground during one of those fleeting visits he made back to England in his old age; that they had at least linked syllables in the parish of his birth, London North Seven, which is not in Highgate Village, as Samuel Taylor Coleridge could have wished.

Elsewhere in the *Bundle* does Miss Hargreaves disclose her natural affinity with Mr. Lear, and reveal that her talents at least bear comparison with his in her Tennysonian ear for the music of words:

> *Cleft in the narrow gulf of gusty grief*
> *My soul is like a cricket on a leaf . . .*

And most especially in 'Halcyon Days' which were:

> *Wrapped in high summer's indigenous haze . . .*

But it would be unseemlious in the extreme to extol the merits of one poet (even though almost unknown) while I am only to be concerned with inviting the reader into the pages of another, and a greater. If there could be any excuse for beginning to make such comparison it resides in the magical name of Margaret Rutherford, whose book of Lear this is. From Cape Kennedy to Tooting Bec, from Bunbury (Western Australia) to Beaconsfield, Miss Rutherford, through film-land and the stage, is famed and loved as the harbinger of a humour which is altogether without malice, which tenderly yet firmly presents the absurd and always reveals the eternal values behind it. When time can be spared from the exigencies of the studio and the cries of the call-boy her poetry readings take a high place in her full life and delight her public. Through her, Edward Lear has made even more friends than he had before. And as to Constance Hargreaves—it was her spirit that opened the way to a friendship of twenty years standing and brought us together in a country we have in common.

I like to imagine Margaret Rutherford making an informal call at the Villa Tennyson. There would be no need for her to knock twice on the door; no need for her to ask for an introduction to Mr. and Mrs. Discobbolos, to be allowed to commiserate with the Pobble on the condition of his feet, or to take a trip to the Coast of Coromandel in the hope of having a few words with the Yonghy Bonghy Bò. All these interesting people, and many others, would be available to her. And I do not believe there could be any greater pleasure for Edward than to curl up his long legs, settle in his favourite chair, and listen to Margaret's beautiful voice reading to him from his moon-marvellous works. Even Foss would approve.

Since Foss cannot purr as you open this book, nor an attendant tape-recorder offer you Margaret Rutherford's *truly* inimitable readings as you turn the pages, there is nothing for it, Reader, there is nothing for it : whether you buy it, borrow it, copy it, or steal it—whether you know Mr. Lear better than you know your own mind, or the psychiatrists do—on your most personal shelves, near to your bed I hope, this paperback must be.

FRANK BAKER

NONSENSE STORIES

THE STORY OF THE FOUR LITTLE CHILDREN
WHO WENT ROUND THE WORLD

Once upon a time, a long while ago, there were four little people whose names were

VIOLET,   SLINGSBY,   GUY,   AND LIONEL;

and they all thought they should like to see the world. So they bought a large boat to sail quite round the world by sea, and then they were to come back on the other side by land. The boat was painted blue with green spots, and the sail was yellow with red stripes; and when they set off, they only took a small Cat to steer and look after the boat, besides an elderly Quangle-Wangle, who had to cook the dinner and make the tea; for which purposes they took a large kettle.

19

For the first ten days they sailed on beautifully, and found plenty to eat, as there were lots of fish, and they had only to take them out of the sea with a long spoon, when the Quangle-Wangle instantly cooked them, and the Pussy-cat was fed with the bones, with which she expressed herself pleased on the whole, so that all the party were very happy.

During the day-time, Violet chiefly occupied herself in putting salt-water into a churn, while her three brothers churned it violently, in the hope that it would turn into butter, which it seldom, if ever did; and in the evening they all retired into the Tea-kettle, where they all managed to sleep very comfortably, while Pussy and the Quangle-Wangle managed the boat.

After a time they saw some land at a distance; and when they came to it, they found it was an island made of water quite surrounded by earth. Besides that, it was bordered by evanescent isthmusses with a great Gulf-stream running about all over it, so that it was perfectly beautiful, and contained only a single tree, 503 feet high.

When they had landed, they walked about, but found to their great surprise, that the island was quite full of veal-cutlets and chocolate-drops, and nothing else. So they all climbed up the single high tree to discover, if possible, if there were any people; but having remained on the top of the tree for a week, and not seeing anybody, they naturally concluded that there were no inhabitants, and accordingly when they came down, they loaded the boat with two thousand veal-cutlets and a million of chocolate drops, and these afforded them sustenance for more than a month, during which time they pursued their voyage with the utmost delight and apathy.

After this they came to a shore where there were no less than sixty-five great red parrots with blue tails, sitting on a rail all of a row, and all fast asleep. And I am sorry to say that the Pussy-cat and the Quangle-Wangle crept softly and bit off the tail-feathers of all the sixty-five parrots, for which Violet reproved them both severely.

Notwithstanding which, she proceeded to insert all the feathers, two hundred and sixty in number, in her bonnet,

thereby causing it to have a lovely and glittering appearance, highly prepossessing and efficatious.

The next thing that happened to them was in a narrow part of the sea, which was so entirely full of fishes that the boat could go on no further; so they remained there about six weeks, till they had eaten nearly all the fishes, which were Soles, and all ready-cooked and covered with shrimp sauce, so that there was no trouble whatever. And as the few fishes who remained uneaten complained of the cold, as well as of the difficulty they had in getting any sleep on account of the extreme noise made by the Arctic Bears and the Tropical Turnspits which frequented the neighbourhood in great numbers, Violet most amiably knitted a small wollen frock for several of the fishes, and Slingsby administered some opium drops to them, through which kindness they became quite warm and slept soundly.

Then they came to a country which was wholly covered with immense Orange-trees of a vast size, and quite full of fruit. So they all landed, taking with them the Tea-kettle, intending to gather some of the Oranges and place them in it. But while they were busy about this, a most dreadfully high wind rose, and blew out most of the Parrot-tail feathers from Violet's bonnet. That, however, was nothing compared with the calamity of the Oranges falling down on

their heads by millions and millions, which thumped and bumped and bumped and thumped them all so seriously that they were obliged to run as hard as they could for their lives, besides that the sound of the Oranges rattling on the Tea-kettle was of the most fearful and amazing nature.

Nevertheless they got safely to the boat, although considerably vexed and hurt; and the Quangle-Wangle's right

foot was so knocked about, that he had to sit with his head in his slipper for at least a week.

This event made them all for a time rather melancholy, and perhaps they might never have become less so, had not Lionel with a most praiseworthy devotion and perseverance, continued to stand on one leg and whistle to them in a loud

and lively manner, which diverted the whole party so extremely, that they gradually recovered their spirits, and agreed that whenever they should reach home they would subscribe towards a testimonial to Lionel, entirely made of Gingerbread and Raspberries, as an earnest token of their sincere and grateful infection.

After sailing on calmly for several more days, they came to another country, where they were much pleased and surprised to see a countless multitude of white Mice with red eyes, all sitting in a great circle, slowly eating Custard Pudding with the most satisfactory and polite demeanour.

And as the four Travellers were rather hungry, being tired of eating nothing but Soles and Oranges for so long a period, they held a council as to the propriety of asking the

Mice for some of their Pudding in a humble and affecting manner, by which they could hardly be otherwise than gratified. It was agreed therefore that Guy should go and ask the Mice, which he immediately did; and the result was that they gave a Walnut-shell only half full of Custard diluted with water. Now, this displeased Guy, who said, 'Out of such a lot of Pudding as you have got, I must say you might have spared a somewhat larger quantity!' But

25

no sooner had he finished speaking than all the Mice turned round at once, and sneezed at him in an appalling and vindictive manner, (and it is impossible to imagine a more scroobious and unpleasant sound than that caused by the simultaneous sneezing of many millions of angry Mice,) so

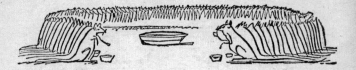

that Guy rushed back to the boat, having first shied his cap into the middle of the Custard Pudding, by which means he completely spoiled the Mice's dinner.

By-and-by the Four Children came to a country where there were no houses, but only an incredibly innumerable number of large bottles without corks, and of a dazzling and sweetly susceptible blue colour. Each of these blue bottles contained a Blue-Bottle Fly, and all these interesting animals live continually together in the most copious and rural

harmony, nor perhaps in many parts of the world is such perfect and abject happiness to be found. Violet, and Slingsby, and Guy, and Lionel, were greatly struck with this singular and instructive settlement, and having previously asked permission of the Blue-Bottle-Flies (which was most courteously granted), the Boat was drawn up to the shore and they proceeded to make tea in front of the Bottles; but as they had no tea-leaves, they merely placed some pebbles in the hot water, and the Quangle-Wangle played some tunes over it on an Accordion, by which of course tea was made directly, and of the very best quality.

The Four Children then entered into conversation with the Blue-Bottle Flies, who discoursed in a placid and genteel manner, though with a slightly buzzing accent, chiefly owing to the fact that they each held a small clothes-brush

between their teeth which naturally occasioned a fizzy extraneous utterance.

'Why,' said Violet, 'would you kindly inform us, do you reside in bottles? and if in bottles at all, why not rather in green or purple, or indeed in yellow bottles?'

To which questions a very aged Blue-Bottle-Fly answered, 'We found the bottles here all ready to live in, that is to say, our great-great-great-great-great-grandfathers did, so we occupied them at once. And when the winter comes on, we turn the bottles upside-down, and consequently rarely feel the cold at all, and you know very well that this could not be the case with bottles of any other colour than blue.'

'Of course it could not;' said Slingsby, 'but if we may take the liberty of inquiring, on what do you chiefly subsist?'

'Mainly on Oyster-patties,' said the Blue-Bottle-Fly, 'and, when these are scarce, on Raspberry Vinegar and Russian leather boiled down to a jelly.'

'How delicious!' said Guy.

To which Lionel added, 'Huzz!' and all the Blue-Bottle-Flies said 'Buzz!'

At this time, an elderly Fly said it was the hour for the Evening-song to be sung; and on a signal being given all the Blue-Bottle-Flies began to buzz at once in a sumptuous and sonorous manner, the melodious and mucilaginous sounds

27

echoing all over the waters, and resounding across the tumultuous tops of the transitory Titmice upon the intervening and verdant mountains, with a serene and sickly suavity only known to the truly virtuous. The Moon was shining slobaciously from the star-bespringled sky, while her light irrigated the smooth and shiny sides and wings and backs of the Blue-Bottle-Flies with a peculiar and trivial splendour, while all nature cheerfully responded to the cerulæan and conspicuous circumstances.

In many long-after years, the four little Travellers looked back to that evening as one of the happiest in all their lives, and it was already past midnight, when—the Sail of the Boat having been set up by the Quangle-Wangle, the Tea-kettle and Churn placed in their respective positions, and the Pussy-cat stationed at the Helm—the Children each took a last and affectionate farewell of the Blue-Bottle-Flies, who walked down in a body to the water's edge to see the Travellers embark.

As a token of parting respect and esteem, Violet made a curtsey quite down to the ground, and stuck one of her few

remaining Parrot-tail feathers into the back hair of the most pleasing of the Blue-Bottle-Flies, while Slingsby, Guy, and Lionel offered them three small boxes, containing respectivly, Black Pins, Dried Figs, and Epsom Salts : and thus they left that happy shore for ever.

Overcome by their feelings, the Four little Travellers instantly jumped into the Tea-kettle, and fell fast asleep.

But all along the shore for many hours there was distinctly heard a sound of severely suppressed sobs, and of a vague multitude of living creatures using their pocket-handkerchiefs in a subdued simultaneous snuffle—lingering sadly along the wallopping waves as the boat sailed farther and farther away from the Land of the Happy Blue-Bottle-Flies.

Nothing particular occurred for some days after these events, except that as the Travellers were passing a low tract of sand, they perceived an unusual and gratifying spectacle, namely, a large number of Crabs and Crawfish—perhaps six or seven hundred—sitting by the water-side, and endeavouring to disentangle a vast heap of pale pink worsted, which they moistened at intervals with a fluid composed of Lavender-water and White-wine Negus.

'Can we be of any service to you, O crusty Crabbies?' said the Four Children.

'Thank you kindly,' said the Crabs, consecutively. 'We are trying to make some worsted Mittens, but do not know how.'

On which Violet, who was perfectly acquainted with the are of mitten-making, said to the Crabs, 'Do your claws unscrew, or are they fixtures?'

'They are all made to unscrew,' said the Crabs, and forthwith they deposited a great pile of claws close to the boat, with which Violet uncombed all the pale pink worsted, and then made the loveliest Mittens with it you can imagine. These the Crabs, having resumed and screwed on their claws, placed cheerfully upon their wrists, and walked away rapidly on their hind-legs, warbling songs with a silvery voice and in a minor key.

After this the four little people sailed on again till they came to a vast and wide plain of astonishing dimensions, on which nothing whatever could be discovered at first; but as the Travellers walked onward, there appeared in the extreme and dim distance a single object, which on a nearer approach and on an accurately cutaneous inspection, seemed to be somebody in a large white wig sitting on an arm-chair made of Sponge Cakes and Oyster-shells. 'It does not quite look like a human being,' said Violet, doubtfully; nor could they make out what it really was, till the Quangle-Wangle (who had previously been round the world), exclaimed softly in a loud voice, 'It is the Co-operative Cauliflower!'

And so in truth it was, and they soon found that what they had taken for an immense wig was in reality the top of the cauliflower, and that he had no feet at all, being able to walk tolerably well with a fluctuating and graceful movement on a single cabbage stalk, an accomplishment which naturally saved him the expense of stockings and shoes.

Presently, while the whole party from the boat was gazing at him with mingled affection and disgust, he suddenly arose, and in a somewhat plumdomphious manner hurried off towards the setting sun,—his steps supported by two superincumbent confidential cucumbers, and a large number of Waterwagtails proceeding in advance of him by three-and-three in a row—till he finally disappeared on the brink of the western sky in a crystal cloud of sudorific sand.

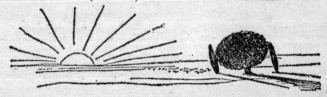

So remarkable a sight of course impressed the Four Children very deeply; and they returned immediately to their boat with a strong sense of undeveloped asthma and a great appetite.

Shortly after this the Travellers were obliged to sail directly below some high overhanging rocks, from the top of one of which, a particularly odious little boy, dressed in rose-coloured knickerbockers, and with a pewter plate upon his head, threw an enormous Pumpkin at the boat, by which it was instantly upset.

But this upsetting was of no consequence, because all the party knew how to swim very well, and in fact they preferred swimming about till after the moon rose, when the water growing chilly, they sponge-taneously entered the boat. Meanwhile the Quangle-Wangle threw back the Pumpkin with immense force, so that it hit the rocks where the malicious little boy in rose-coloured knickerbockers was sitting, when, being quite full of Lucifer-matches, the Pumpkin exploded surreptitiously into a thousand bits, whereon the rocks instantly took fire, and the odious little

boy became unpleasantly hotter and hotter and hotter, till his knickerbockers were turned quite green, and his nose was burned off.

Two or three days after this had happened, they came to another place, where they found nothing at all except some wide and deep pits full of Mulbery Jam. This is the property of the tiny Yellow-nosed Apes who abound in these districts, and who store up the Mulberry Jam for their food in winter, when they mix it with pellucid pale periwinkle soup, and serve it out in Wedgwood China bowls, which grow freely all over that part of the country. Only one of the Yellow-nosed Apes was on the spot, and he was fast asleep: yet the Four Travellers and the Quangle-Wangle and Pussy were so terrified by the violence and sanguinary sound of his snoring, that they merely took a small cupful of the Jam, and returned to re-embark in their Boat without delay.

What was their horror on seeing the boat (including the Churn and the Tea-kettle), in the mouth of an enormous Seeze Pyder, an aquatic and ferocious creature truly dreadful to behold, and happily only met with in those excessive longitudes. In a moment the beautiful boat was bitten into fifty-five-thousand-million-hundred-billion bits, and it in-

stantly became quite clear that Violet, Slingsby, Guy, and Lionel could no longer preliminate their voyage by sea.

The Four Travellers were therefore obliged to resolve on pursuing their wanderings by land, and very fortunately there happened to pass by at that moment, an elderly Rhinoceros, on which they seized; and all four mounting on his back, the Quangle-Wangle sitting on his horn and holding on by his ears, and the Pussy-cat swinging at the end of his tail, they set off, having only four small beans and three pounds of mashed potatoes to last through their whole journey.

They were, however, able to catch numbers of the chickens and turkeys, and other birds who incessantly alighted on the head of the Rhinoceros for the purpose of gathering the seeds of the rhododendron plants which grew there, and these creatures they cooked in the most translucent and satisfactory manner, by means of a fire lighted on the end of the Rhinoceros' back. A crowd of Kangaroos and Gigantic Cranes accompanied them, from feelings of curiosity and complacency, so that they were never at a loss for company, and went onward as it were in a sort of profuse and triumphant procession.

Thus, in less than eighteen weeks, they all arrived safely at home, where they were received by their admiring relatives with joy tempered with contempt; and where they finally resolved to carry out the rest of their travelling plans at some more favourable opportunity.

As for the Rhinoceros, in token of their grateful adherence they had him killed and stuffed directly, and then set him up outside the door of their father's house as a Diaphanous Doorscraper.

B

THE OWL AND THE PUSSY-CAT

I

The Owl and the Pussy-cat went to sea
  In a beautiful pea-green boat,
They took some honey, and plenty of money,
  Wrapped up in a five-pound note.
The Owl looked up to the stars above,
  And sang to a small guitar,
'O lovely Pussy! O Pussy, my love,
    What a beautiful Pussy you are,
        You are,
        You are!
  What a beautiful Pussy you are!'

34

II

Pussy said to the Owl, 'You elegant fowl!
  How charmingly sweet you sing!
O let us be married! too long we have tarried:
  But what shall we do for a ring?'
They sailed away, for a year and a day,
  To the land where the Bong-tree grows
And there in a wood a Piggy-wig stood
  With a ring at the end of his nose,
      His nose,
      His nose,
  With a ring at the end of his nose.

III

'Dear Pig, are you willing to sell for one shilling
  Your ring?' Said the Piggy, 'I will.'
So they took it away, and were married next day
  By the Turkey who lives on the hill.
They dined on mince, and slices of quince,
  Which they ate with a runcible spoon;

And hand in hand, on the edge of the sand,
They danced by the light of the moon,
　　The moon,
　　The moon,
They danced by the light of the moon.

THE JUMBLIES

They went to sea in a Sieve, they did,
  In a Sieve they went to sea :
In spite of all their friends could say,
On a winter's morn, on a stormy day,
  In a Sieve they went to sea !
And when the Sieve turned round and round,
And every one cried, 'You'll all be drowned !'
They called aloud, 'Our Sieve ain't big,
But we don't care a button ! we don't care a fig !
  In a Sieve we'll go to sea !'
    Far and few, far and few,
      Are the lands where the Jumblies live ;
      Their heads are green, and their hands are blue,
        And they went to sea in a Sieve.

II

They sailed away in a Sieve, they did,
   In a Sieve they sailed so fast,
With only a beautiful pea-green veil.
Tied with a riband by way of a sail,
   To a small tobacco-pipe mast;
And every one said, who saw them go,
'O won't they be soon upset, you know!
For the sky is dark, and the voyage is long,
And happen what may, it's extremely wrong
   In a Sieve to sail so fast!'
     Far and few, far and few,
      Are the lands where the Jumblies live;
     Their heads are green, and their hands are blue,
      And they went to sea in a Sieve.

III

The water it soon came in, it did,
   The water it soon came in;
So to keep them dry, they wrapped their feet
In a pinky paper all folded neat,
   And they fastened it down with a pin.
And they passed the night in a crockery-jar,
And each of them said, 'How wise we are!
Though the sky be dark, and the voyage be long,
Yet we never can think we were rash or wrong,
   While round in our Sieve we spin!'
     Far and few, far and few,
      Are the lands where the Jumblies live;
     Their heads are green, and their hands are blue,
      And they went to sea in a Sieve.

IV

And all night long they sailed away;
  And when the sun went down,
They whistled and warbled a moony song
To the echoing sound of a coppery gong,
  In the shade of the mountains brown.
'O Timballo! How happy we are,
When we live in a sieve and a crockery-jar,
And all night long in the moonlight pale,
We sail away with a pea-green sail,
  In the shade of the mountains brown!'
    Far and few, far and few,
      Are the lands where the Jumblies live;
    Their heads are green, and their hands are blue,
      And they went to sea in a Sieve.

V

They sailed to the Western Sea, they did,
  To a land all covered with trees,
And they bought an Owl, and a useful Cart,
And a pound of Rice, and a Cranberry Tart,
  And a hive of silvery Bees.
And they bought a Pig, and some green Jack-daws,
And a lovely Monkey with lollipop paws,
And forty bottles of Ring-Bo-Ree,
  And no end of Stilton Cheese.
    Far and few, far and few,
      Are the lands where the Jumblies live;
    Their heads are green, and their hands are blue,
      And they went to sea in a Sieve.

And in twenty years they all came back,
  In twenty years or more,
And every one said, 'How tall they've grown!
For they've been to the Lakes, and the Torrible Zone,
  And the hills of the Chankly Bore;
And they drank their health, and gave them a feast
Of dumplings made of beautiful yeast;
And every one said, 'If we only live,
We too will go to sea in a Sieve,—
  To the hills of the Chankly Bore!'
    Far and few, far and few,
      Are the lands where the Jumblies live;
      Their heads are green, and their hands are blue,
        And they went to sea in a Sieve.

THE CUMMERBUND

AN INDIAN POEM

I

She sate upon her Dobie,
  To watch the Evening Star,
And all the Punkahs as they passed,
  Cried, 'My! how fair you are!'
Around her bower, with quivering leaves
  The tall Kamsamahs grew,
And Kitmutgars in wild festoons
  Hung down from Tchokis blue.

II

Below her home the river rolled
  With soft meloobious sound,
Where golden-finned Chuprassies swam,
  In myriads circling round.
Above, on tallest trees remote
  Green Ayahs perched alone,
And all night long the Mussak moan'd
  Its melancholy tone.

III

And where the purple Nullahs threw
  Their branches far and wide,—

And silvery Goreewallahs flew
  In silence, side by side,—
The little Bheesties' twittering cry
  Rose on the flagrant air,
And oft the angry Jampan howled
  Deep in his hateful lair.

IV

She sate upon her Dobie,—
  She heard the Nimmak hum,—
When all at once a cry arose,—
  'The Cummerbund is come!'
In vain she fled :—with open jaws
  The angry monster followed,
And so, (before assistance came,)
  That Lady Fair was swollowed.

V

They sought in vain for even a bone
  Respectfully to bury,—
They said,—'Hers was a dreadful fate!'
  (And Echo answered 'Very.')
They nailed her Dobie to the wall,
  Where last her form was seen,
And underneath they wrote these words,
  In yellow, blue, and green :—

Beware, ye Fair! Ye Fair, beware!
  Nor sit out late at night,—
Lest horrid Cummerbunds should come,
  And swollow you outright.

NOTE.—First published in *Times of India*, Bombay, July, 1874.

THE AKOND OF SWAT

Who, or why, or which, or *what*, Is the Akond of SWAT?
Is he tall or short, or dark or fair?
Does he sit on a stool or a sofa or chair, or SQUAT,
                    The Akond of Swat?

Is he wise or foolish, young or old?
Does he drink his soup and his coffee cold, or HOT,
                    The Akond of Swat?

Does he sing or whistle, jabber or talk,
And when riding abroad does he gallop or walk,
                        or TROT,
                    The Akond of Swat?

Does he wear a turban, a fez, or a hat?
Does he sleep on a mattress, a bed, or a mat, or a COT,
                    The Akond of Swat?

When he writes a copy in round-hand size,
Does he cross his T's and finish his I's with a DOT,
                    The Akond of Swat?

Can he write a letter concisely clear
Without a speck or a smudge or smear or BLOT,
                    The Akond of Swat?

Do his people like him extremely well?
Or do they, whenever they can, rebel or PLOT,
                    At the Akond of Swat?

If he catches them then, either old or young,
Does he have them chopped in pieces or hung,

> or shot,
> The Akond of Swat?

Do his people prig in the lanes or park?
Or even at times, when days are dark,   GAROTTE?

> O the Akond of Swat!

Does he study the wants of his own dominion?
Or doesn't he care for public opinion   a JOT,

> The Akond of Swat?

To amuse his mind do his people show him
Pictures, or any one's last new poem,   or WHAT,

> For the Akond of Swat?

At night if he suddenly screams and wakes,
Do they bring him only a few small cakes,   or a LOT,

> For the Akond of Swat?

Does he live on turnips, tea, or tripe?
Does he like his shawl to be marked with a stripe,

> or a DOT,
> The Akond of Swat?

Does he like to lie on his back in a boat
Like the lady who lived in that isle remote, SHALLOTT,

> The Akond of Swat?

Is he quiet, or always making a fuss?
Is his steward a Swiss or a Swede or a Russ, or a SCOT,

> The Akond of Swat?

Does he like to sit by the calm blue wave?
Or to sleep and snore in a dark green cave, or a GROTT,

> The Akond of Swat?

Does he drink small beer from a silver jug?
Or a bowl? or a glass? or a cup? or a mug? or a POT,
                    The Akond of Swat?

Does he beat his wife with a gold-topped pipe,
When she lets the gooseberries grow too ripe, or ROT,
                    The Akond of Swat?

Does he wear a white tie when he dines with friends,
And tie it neat in a bow with ends,   or a KNOT,
                    The Akond of Swat?

Does he like new cream, and hate mince-pies?
When he looks at the sun does he wink his eyes,
                      or NOT,
                    The Akond of Swat?

Does he teach his subjects to roast and bake?
Does he sail about on an inland lake,   in a YACHT,
                    The Akond of Swat?

Some one, or nobody, knows I wot
Who or which or why or what
                    Is the Akond of Swat!

For the existence of this potentate see Indian newspapers, *passim*.
The proper way to read the verses is to make an immense emphasis on
the monosyllabic rhymes, which indeed ought to be shouted out by a
chorus.

LIMERICKS

I

A BOOK OF NONSENSE

(1846)

There was an Old Man with a beard,
Who said, 'It is just as I feared!—
Two Owls and a Hen, four Larks and a Wren
Have all built their nests in my beard!'

There was an Old Man with a nose,
Who said, 'If you choose to suppose,
    That my nose is too long, you are certainly wrong!'
That remarkable Man with a nose.

There was a Young Lady whose chin,
Resembled the point of a pin;
    So she had it made sharp, and purchased a harp,
And played several tunes with her chin.

There was an Old Man of Apulia,
Whose conduct was very peculiar
He fed twenty sons, upon nothing but buns,
That whimsical Man of Apulia,

There was an Old Person of Mold,
Who shrank from sensations of cold;
So he purchased some muffs, some furs and some fluffs,
And wrapped himself from the cold.

There was an Old Man of Peru,
Who watched his wife making a stew;
But once by mistake, in a stove she did bake,
That unfortunate Man of Peru.

There was an Old Man of Cape Horn,
Who wished he had never been born;
So he sat on a chair, till he died of despair,
That dolorous Man of Cape Horn.

There was an Old Man of Corfu,
Who never knew what he should do;
So he rushed up and down, till the sun made him brown,
That bewildered Old Man of Corfu.

There was an Old Person of Cromer,
Who stood on one leg to read Homer;
When he found he grew stiff, he jumped over the cliff,
Which concluded that Person of Cromer.

53

There was an Old Man of Dundee,
Who frequented the top of a tree;
When disturbed by the crows, he abruptly arose,
And exclaimed, 'I'll return to Dundee.'

There was an Old Person of Tring,
Who embellished his nose with a ring;
He gazed at the moon, every evening in June,
That ecstatic Old Person of Tring.

There was an Old Man on some rocks,
Who shut his wife up in a box,
When she said, 'Let me out,' he exclaimed,
    'Without doubt,
You will pass all your life in that box.'

NONSENSE ALPHABET I

A

a

A was once an applepie,
  Pidy
  Widy
  Tidy
  Pidy
Nice insidy
Apple Pie.

B

b

B was once a little bear,
  Beary!
  Wary!
  Hairy!
  Beary!
Taky cary!
Little Bear!

C

c

C was once a little cake,
    Caky,
    Baky
    Maky
    Caky,
  Taky Caky,
  Little Cake!

D

d

D was once a little doll,
    Dolly,
    Molly,
    Polly
    Nolly,
  Nursy Dolly,
  Little Doll!

E

e

E was once a little eel,
    Eely
    Weely
    Peely
    Eely
Twirly, Tweely
Little Eel!

F

f

F was once a little fish
    Fishy
    Wishy
    Squishy
    Fishy
In a Dishy
Little Fish!

G

g

G was once a little goose,
    Goosy
    Moosy
    Boosey
    Goosey
Waddly-woosy
Little Goose!

H

h

H was once a little hen,
    Henny
    Chenny
    Tenny
    Henny
Eggsy-any
Little Hen?

I

i

I was once a bottle of ink,
  Inky
  Dinky
  Thinky
  Inky,
 Blacky Minky
 Bottle of Ink!

J

j

J was once a jar of jam,
  Jammy,
  Mammy,
  Clammy,
  Jammy,
Sweety—Swammy,
 Jar of Jam!

K

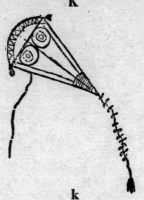

k

K was once a little kite,
    Kity
    Whity
    Flighty
    Kity
Out of Sighty—
Little Kite!

L

l

L was once a little lark,
    Larky!
    Marky!
    Harky!
    Larky!
In the Parky,
Little Lark!

m

M was once a little mouse,
    Mousey
    Bousey
    Sousy
    Mousy,
In the Housy
Little Mouse!

N

n

N was once a little needle,
    Needly
    Tweedly
    Threedly
    Needly
Wisky—wheedly
Little Needle!

C

O

o

O was once a little owl,
    Owly,
    Prowly,
    Howly,
    Owly
  Browny fowly
  Little Owl!

P

p

P was once a little pump,
    Pumpy
    Slumpy
    Flumpy
    Pumpy
  Dumpy, Thumpy
  Little Pump!

q

Q was once a little quail,
  Quaily
  Faily
  Daily
  Quaily
Stumpy-taily
Little Quail!

R

r

R was once a little rose,
  Rosy
  Posy
  Nosy
  Rosy
Blows-y——grows-y
Little Rose!

s

S was once a little shrimp
    Shrimpy
    Nimpy
    Flimpy
    Shrimpy
Jumpy—jimpy
Little Shrimp!

T

t

T was once a little thrush,
    Thrushy!
    Hushy!
    Bushy!
    Thrushy!
Flitty—Flushy—
Little Thrush!

u

U was once a little urn,
    Urny
    Burny
    Turny
    Urny,
Bubbly—burny,
Little Urn.

v

V was once a little vine,
    Viny
    Winy
    Twiny
    Viny
Twisty-twiny
Little Vine !

W

w

W was once a whale,
Whaly
Scaly
Shaly
Whaly
Tumbly-taily
Mighty Whale!

X

x

X was once a great king Xerxes,
Xerxy
Perxy
Turxy
Xerxy
Linxy Lurxy
Great King Xerxes!

70

Y

y

Y was once a little yew,
  Yewdy,
  Fewdy
  Crudy
  Yewdy
Growdy, grewdy,
Little Yew!

Z

z

Z was once a piece of zinc
  Tinky
  Winky
  Blinky
  Tinky
Tinkly Minky
Piece of Zinc!

Bottlephorkia Spoonifolia

Smalltoothcombia Domestica

Bluebottle Buzztilentia

Pollybirdia Singularis

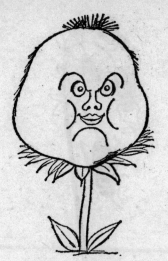

Phattfacia Stupenda

Plumbunnia Nutritiosa

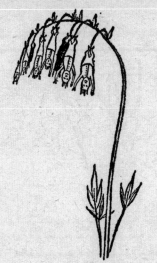

Manypeeplia Upsidownia

Guittara Pensilis

Cockatooca Superba

Baccopipia Gracilis

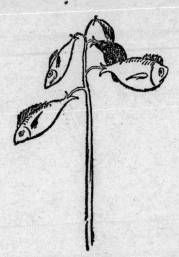

Fishia Marina

Piggiawiggia Pyramidalis

INSECTS, FEATHERS
AND THINGS

MR. AND MRS. SPIKKY SPARROW

I

On a little piece of wood,
Mr. Spikky Sparrow stood;
Mrs. Sparrow sate close by,
A-making of an insect pie,
For her little children five,
In the nest and all alive,
Singing with a cheerful smile
To amuse them all the while,
    Twikky wikky wikky wee,
    Wikky bikky twikky tee,
      Spikky bikky bee!

II

Mrs. Spikky Sparrow said,
'Spikky, Darling! in my head
'Many thoughts of trouble come,
'Like to flies upon a plum!
'All last night, among the trees,
'I heard you cough, I heard you sneeze;

D

'And, thought I, it's come to that
'Because he does not wear a hat!
　'Chippy wippy sikky tee!
　'Bikky wikky tikky mee!
　　'Spikky chippy wee!

III

'Not that you are growing old,
'But the nights are growing cold.
'No one stays out all night long
'Without a hat: I'm sure it's wrong!'
Mr. Spikky said, 'How kind,
'Dear! you are, to speak your mind!
'All your life I wish you luck!
'You are! you are! a lovely duck!
　'Witchy witchy witchy wee!
　　'Twitchy witchy witchy bee!
　　　'Tikky tikky tee!

IV

'I was also sad, and thinking,
'When one day I saw you winking,
'And I heard you sniffle-snuffle,
'And I saw your feathers ruffle;
'To myself I sadly said,
'She's neuralgia in her head!
'That dear head has nothing on it!
'Ought she not to wear a bonnet?
　'Witchy kitchy kitchy wee?
　　'Spikky wikky mikky bee?
　　　'Chippy wippy chee?

V

'Let us both fly up to town!
'There I'll buy you such a gown!
'Which, completely in the fashion,
'You shall tie a sky-blue sash on.
'And a pair of slippers neat,
'To fit your darling little feet,
'So that you will look and feel
'Quite galloobious and genteel!
   'Jikky wikky bikky see,
    'Chicky bikky wikky bee,
     'Twicky witchy wee!'

VI

So they both to London went,
Alighting on the Monument,
Whence they flew down swiftly—pop,
Into Moses' wholesale shop;
There they bought a hat and bonnet,
And a gown with spots upon it,
A satin sash of Cloxam blue,
And a pair of slippers too.
   Zikky wikky mikky bee,
    Witchy witchy mitchy kee,
     Sikky tikky wee.

VII

Then when so completely drest,
Back they flew, and reached their nest.
Their children cried, 'O Ma and Pa!
How truly beautiful you are!'
Said they, 'We trust that cold or pain

'We shall never feel again!
'While, perched on tree, or house, or steeple,
'We now shall look like other people.
   'Witchy witchy witchy wee,
   'Twikky mikky bikky bee,
    'Zikky sikky tee.'

CALICO PIE

I

Calico Pie,
The little Birds fly
Down to the calico tree,
Their wings were blue,
And they sang 'Tilly-loo!'
Till away they flew,—
And they never came back to me!
They never came back!
They never came back!
They never came back to me!

II

Calico Jam,
The little Fish swam,
Over the syllabub sea,
He took off his hat,

To the Sole and the Sprat,
And the Willeby-wat,—
But he never came back to me!

He never came back!
He never came back!
He never came back to me!

III

Calico Ban,
The little Mice ran,
To be ready in time for tea,
Flippity flup,
They drank it all up,
And danced in the cup,—

But they never came back to me!
They never came back!
They never came back!
They never came back to me!

Calico Drum,
The Grasshoppers come,
The Butterfly, Beetle, and Bee,
Over the ground,
Around and round,
With a hop and a bound,—

But they never came back!
They never came back!
They never came back!
They never came back to me!

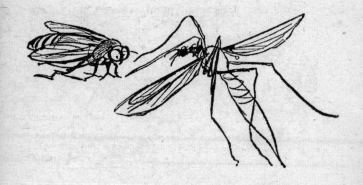

THE DADDY LONG-LEGS
AND THE FLY

I

Once Mr. Daddy Long-legs,
  Dressed in brown and gray,
Walked about upon the sands
  Upon a summer's day;
And there among the pebbles,
  When the wind was rather cold,
He met with Mr. Floppy Fly,
  All dressed in blue and gold.
And as it was too soon to dine,
They drank some Periwinkle-wine,
And played an hour or two, or more,
At battlecock and shuttledore.

II

Said **Mr.** Daddy Long-legs
To Mr. Floppy Fly,
'Why do you never come to court?
   I wish you'd tell me why.
All gold and shine, in dress so fine,
   You'd quite delight the court.
Why do you never go at all?
   I really think you *ought*!
And if you went, you'd see such sights!
Such rugs! and jugs! and candle-lights!
And more than all, the King and Queen,
One in red, and one in green!'

'O Mr. Daddy Long-legs,'
   Said Mr. Floppy Fly,
'It's true I never go to court,
   And I will tell you why.
If I had six long legs like yours,
   At once I'd go to court!
But oh! I can't, because *my* legs
   Are so extremely short.
And I'm afraid the King and Queen
(One in red, and one in green)
Would say aloud, "You are not fit,
You Fly, to come to court a bit!"

IV

'O Mr. Daddy Long-Legs,'
   Said Mr. Floppy Fly,
'I wish you'd sing one little song!
   One mumbian melody!

You used to sing so awful well
    In former days gone by,
But now you never sing at all;
    I wish you'd tell me why:
For if you would, the silvery sound
Would please the shrimps and cockles round,
And all the crabs would gladly come
To hear you sing, "Ah, Hum di Hum"!'

V

Said Mr. Daddy Long-legs,
    'I can never sing again!
And if you wish, I'll tell you why,
    Although it gives me pain.
For years I cannot hum a bit,
    Or sing the smallest song;
And this the dreadful reason is,
    My legs are grown too long!
My six long legs, all here and there,
Oppress my bosom with despair;
And if I stand, or lie, or sit,
I cannot sing one single bit!'

VI

So Mr. Daddy Long-legs
    And Mr. Floppy Fly
Sat down in silence by the sea,
    And gazed upon the sky.
They said, 'This is a dreadful thing!
The world has all gone wrong,
Since one has legs too short by half,
    The other much too long!
One never more can go to court,
Because his legs have grown too short;
The other cannot sing a song,
    Because his legs have grown too long!'

90

Then Mr. Daddy Long-legs
    And Mr. Floppy Fly
Rushed downward to the foamy sea
    With one sponge-taneous cry;
And there they found a little boat,
    Whose sails were pink and gray;
And off they sailed among the waves,
    Far, and far away.
They sailed across the silent main,
And reached the great Gromboolian plain;
And there they play for evermore
At battlecock and shuttledoor.

THE DONG WITH A
LUMINOUS NOSE

When awful darkness and silence reign
Over the great Gromboolian plain,
  Through the long, long wintry nights;—
When the angry breakers roar
As they beat on the rocky shore;—
  When Storm-clouds brood on the towering heights
Of the Hills of the Chankly Bore :—

Then, through the vast and gloomy dark,
There moves what seems a fiery spark,
  A lonely spark with silvery rays
  Piercing the coal-black night,—
  A Meteor strange and bright :—
Hither and thither the vision strays,
  A single lurid light.

92

Slowly it wanders,—pauses,—creeps,—
Anon it sparkles,—flashes and leaps;
And ever as onward it gleaming goes
A light on the Bong-tree stems it throws.
And those who watch at that midnight hour
From Hall or Terrace, or lofty Tower,
Cry, as the wild light passes along,—
    'The Dong!—the Dong!
  'The wandering Dong through the forest goes!
    'The Dong! the Dong!
 'The Dong with a luminous Nose!'

    Long years ago
  The Dong was happy and gay,
Till he fell in love with a Jumbly Girl
  Who came to those shores one day,
For the Jumblies came in a sieve, they did,—
Landing at eve near the Zemmery Fidd
    Where the Oblong Oysters grow,
  And the rocks are smooth and gray.
And all the woods and the valleys rang
With the Chorus they daily and nightly sang,—
    'Far and few, far and few,
    Are the lands where the Jumblies live;
    Their heads are green, and their hands are blue
    And they went to sea in a sieve.'

Happily, happily passed those days!
    While the cheerful Jumblies staid;
  They danced in circlets all night long,
  To the plaintive pipe of the lively Dong,
    In moonlight, shine, or shade.
For day and night he was always there
By the side of the Jumbly Girl so fair,
With her sky-blue hands, and her sea-green hair.
Till the morning came of that hateful day
When the Jumblies sailed in their sieve away,

And the Dong was left on the cruel shore
Gazing—gazing for evermore,—
Ever keeping his weary eyes on
That pea-green sail on the far horizon,—
Singing the Jumbly Chorus still
As he sate all day on the grassy hill,—

> 'Far and few, far and few,
> Are the lands where the Jumblies live;
> Their heads are green, and their hands are blue,
> And they went to sea in a sieve.'

But when the sun was low in the West,
  The Dong arose and said;—
—'What little sense I once possessed
  Has quite gone out of my head!'—
And since that day he wanders still
By lake and forest, marsh and hill,
Singing—'O somewhere, in valley or plain
'Might I find my Jumbly Girl again!
'For ever I'll seek by lake and shore
'Till I find my Jumbly Girl once more!'

> Playing a pipe with silvery squeaks,
> Since then his Jumbly Girl he seeks,
> And because by night he could not see,
> He gathered the bark of the Twangum Tree
>   On the flowery plain that grows.
>   And he wove him a wondrous Nose,—
> A Nose as strange as a Nose could be!

Of vast proportions and painted red,
And tied with cords to the back of his head.
  —In a hollow rounded space it ended
      With a luminous Lamp within suspended,
  All fenced about
  With a bandage stout
  To prevent the wind from blowing it out;—
And with holes all round to send the light,
In gleaming rays on the dismal night.

And now each night, and all night long,
Over those plains still roams the Dong;
And above the wail of the Chimp and Snipe
You may hear the squeak of his plaintive pipe
While ever he seeks, but seeks in vain
To meet with his Jumbly Girl again;
Lonely and wild—all night he goes,—
The Dong with a luminous Nose!
And all who watch at the midnight hour,
From Hall or Terrace, or lofty Tower,
Cry, as they trace the Meteor bright,
Moving along through the dreary night,—
  'This is the hour when forth he goes,
  'The Dong with a luminous Nose!
  'Yonder—over the plain he goes;
   'He goes!
   'He goes;
  'The Dong with a luminous Nose!'

THE TABLE AND THE CHAIR

I

Said the Table to the Chair,
'You can hardly be aware,
'How I suffer from the heat,
'And from chilblains on my feet!
'If we took a little walk,
'We might have a little talk!
'Pray let us take the air!'
Said the Table to the Chair.

II

Said the Chair unto the Table,
'Now you *know* we are not able!
'How foolishly you talk,
'When you know we *cannot* walk!'
Said the Table, with a sigh,

96

'It can do no harm to try,
'I've as many legs as you,
'Why can't we walk on two?'

III

So they both went slowly down,
And walked about the town
With a cheerful bumpy sound,
As they toddled round and round.
And everybody cried,
As they hastened to their side,
'See! the Table and the Chair
'Have come out to take the air!'

IV

But in going down an alley,
To a castle in a valley,
They completely lost their way,
And wandered all the day,

Till, to see them safely back,
They paid a Ducky-quack,
And a Beetle, and a Mouse,
Who took them to their house.

E

Then they whispered to each other,
'O delightful little brother!
'What a lovely walk we've taken!
'Let us dine on Beans and Bacon!'
So the Ducky, and the leetle
Browny-Mousy and the Beetle
Dined, and danced upon their heads
Till they toddled to their beds.

THE PELICAN CHORUS

King and Queen of the Pelicans we;
No other Birds so grand we see!
None but we have feet like fins!
With lovely leathery throats and chins!
    Ploffskin, Pluffskin, Pelican jee!
    We think no Birds so happy as we!
    Plumpskin, Ploshkin, Pelican jill!
    We think so then, and we thought so still!

We live on the Nile. The Nile we love.
By night we sleep on the cliffs above;
By day we fish, and at eve we stand.
On long bare islands of yellow sand.
And when the sun sinks slowly down
And the great rock walls grow dark and brown,
Where the purple river rolls fast and dim
And the Ivory Ibis starlike skim,

Wing to wing we dance around,—
Stamping our feet with a flumpy sound,—
Opening our mouths as Pelicans ought,
And this is the song we nightly snort;—
 Ploffskin, Pluffskin, Pelican jee,—
 We think no Birds so happy as we!
 Plumpskin, Ploshkin, Pelican jill,—
 We think so then, and we thought so still.

Last year came out our Daughter, Dell;
And all the Birds received her well.
To do her honour, a feast we made
For every bird that can swim or wade.
Herons and Gulls, and Cormorants black,
Cranes, and Flamingoes with scarlet back,
Plovers and Storks, and Geese in clouds,
Swans and Dilberry Ducks in crowds.
Thousands of Birds in wondrous flight!
They ate and drank and danced all night,
And echoing back from the rocks you heard
Multitude-echoes from Bird and Bird,—
 Ploffskin, Pluffskin, Pelican jee!
 We think no Birds so happy as we!
 Plumpskin, Ploshkin, Pelican jill,
 We think so then, and we thought so still!

Yes, they came; and among the rest,
The King of the Cranes all grandly dressed.
Such a lovely tail! Its feathers float
Between the ends of his blue dress-coat;
With pea-green trowsers all so neat,
And a delicate frill to hide his feet,—
(For though no one speaks of it, every one knows,
He has got no webs between his toes!)

As soon as he saw our Daughter Dell,
In violent love that Crane King fell,—
On seeing her waddling form so fair,

With a wreath of shrimps in her short white hair.
And before the end of the next long day,
Our Dell had given her heart away;
For the King of the Cranes had won that heart,
With a Crocodile's egg and a large fish-tart.
She vowed to marry the King of the Cranes,
Leaving the Nile for stranger plains;
And away they flew in a gathering crowd
Of endless birds in a lengthening cloud.
> Ploffskin, Pluffskin, Pelican jee!
> We think no Birds so happy as we!
> Plumpskin, Ploshkin, Pelican jill,
> We think so then, and we thought so still!

And far away in the twilight sky,
We heard them singing a lessening cry,—
Farther and farther till out of sight,
And we stood alone in the silent night!
Often since, in the nights of June,
We sit on the sand and watch the moon;—
She has gone to the great Gromboolian plain,
And we probably never shall meet again!
Oft, in the long still nights of June,
We sit on the rocks and watch the moon;—
——She dwells by the streams of the Chankly Bore,
And we probably never shall see her more.
> Ploffskin, Pluffskin, Pelican jee!
> We think no Birds so happy as we!
> Plumpskin, Ploshkin, Pelican jill,
> We think so then, and we thought so still!

THE COURTSHIP OF THE
YONGHY-BONGHY-BO

I

On the Coast of Coromandel
Where the early pumpkins blow,
In the middle of the woods
  Lived the Yonghy-Bonghy-Bò.
Two old chairs, and half a candle,—
One old jug without a handle,—
    These were all his wordly goods :
    In the middle of the woods,
    These were all the wordly goods,
  Of the Yonghy-Bonghy-Bò,
  Of the Yonghy-Bonghy-Bò.

II

Once, among the Bong-trees walking
  Where the early pumpkins blow,
    To a little heap of stones
  Came the Yonghy-Bonghy-Bò.
There he heard a Lady talking,
To some milk-white Hens of Dorking,—
    "Tis the Lady Jingly Jones!
   'On that little heap of stones
   'Sits the Lady Jingly Jones!'
  Said the Yonghy-Bonghy-Bò,
  Said the Yonghy-Bonghy-Bò.

'Lady Jingly! Lady Jingly!
  'Sitting where the pumpkins blow,
    'Will you come and be my wife?'
  Said the Yonghy-Bonghy-Bò.
'I am tired of living singly,—
'On this coast so wild and shingly,—
    'I'm a-weary of my life:
   'If you'll come and be my wife,
   'Quite serene would be my life!'—
  Said the Yonghy-Bonghy-Bò,
  Said the Yonghy-Bonghy-Bò.

IV

'On this Coast of Coromandel,
  'Shrimps and watercresses grow,
    'Prawns are plentiful and cheap,'
  Said the Yonghy-Bonghy-Bò.
'You shall have my Chairs and candle,

'And my jug without a handle!—
 'Gaze upon the rolling deep
 ('Fish is plentiful and cheap)
 'As the sea, my love is deep!'
Said the Yonghy-Bonghy-Bò,
Said the Yonghy-Bonghy-Bò.

V

Lady Jingly answered sadly,
 And her tears began to flow,—
 'Your proposal comes too late,
 'Mr. Yonghy-Bonghy-Bò!
'I would be your wife most gladly!'
(Here she twirled her fingers madly,)
 'But in England I've a mate!
 'Yes! you've asked me far too late,
 'For in England I've a mate,
 'Mr. Yonghy-Bonghy-Bò!
 'Mr. Yonghy-Bonghy-Bò!'

VI

'Mr. Jones—(his name is Handel,—
 'Handel Jones, Esquire, & Co.)
 'Dorking fowls delights to send,
 'Mr. Yonghy-Bonghy-Bò!
'Keep, oh! keep your chairs and candle,
'And your jug without a handle,—
 'I can merely be your friend!
 '—Should my Jones more Dorkings send,
 'I will give you three, my friend!
 'Mr. Yonghy-Bonghy-Bò!
 'Mr. Yonghy-Bonghy-Bò!'

104

VII

'Though you've such a tiny body,
   'And your head so large doth grow,—
      'Though your hat may blow away,
   'Mr. Yonghy-Bonghy-Bò!
'Though you're such a Hoddy Doddy—
'Yet I wish that I could modi-
      'fy the words I needs must say!
      'Will you please to go away?
      'That is all I have to say—
   'Mr. Yonghy-Bonghy-Bò!'
   'Mr. Yonghy-Bonghy-Bò!

VIII

Down the slippery slopes of Myrtle,
   Where the early pumpkins blow,
      To the calm and silent sea
   Fled the Yonghy-Bonghy-Bò.
There, beyond the Bay of Gurtle,
Lay a large and lively Turtle;—

'You're the Cove,' he said, 'for me
'On your back beyond the sea,
'Turtle, you shall carry me!'
Said the Yonghy-Bonghy-Bò,
Said the Yonghy-Bonghy-Bò.

IX

Through the silent-roaring ocean
    Did the Turtle swiftly go;
        Holding fast upon his shell
    Rode the Yonghy-Bonghy-Bò.
With a sad primæval motion
Towards the sunset isles of Boshen
        Still the Turtle bore him well.
        Holding fast upon his shell,
        'Lady Jingly Jones, farewell!'
    Sang the Yonghy-Bonghy-Bò,
    Sang the Yonghy-Bonghy-Bò.

X

From the Coast of Coromandel,
    Did that Lady never go;
        On that heap of stones she mourns
    For the Yonghy-Bonghy-Bò.
On that Coast of Coromandel,
In his jug without a handle
        Still she weeps, and daily moans;
        On that little heap of stones
        To her Dorking Hens she moans,
    For the Yonghy-Bonghy-Bò,
    For the Yonghy-Bonghy-Bò.

THE POBBLE WHO HAS NO TOES

I

The Pobble who has no toes
　　Had once as many as we;
When they said, 'Some day you may lose them all;'—
　　He replied,—'Fish fiddle de-dee!'
And his Aunt Jobiska made him drink,
Lavender water tinged with pink,
For she said, 'The World in general knows
There's nothing so good for a Pobble's toes!'

II

The Pobble who has no toes,
　　Swam across the Bristol Channel;
But before he set out he wrapped his nose,
　　In a piece of scarlet flannel.
For his Aunt Jobiska said, 'No harm
'Can come to his toes if his nose is warm;
'And its perfectly known that a Pobble's toes
'Are safe,—provided he minds his nose.'

The Pobble swam fast and well
   And when boats or ships came near him
He tinkledy-binkledy-winkled a bell
   So that all the world could hear him.
And all the Sailors and Admirals cried,
When they saw him nearing the further side,—
'He has gone to fish, for his Aunt Jobiska's
'Runcible Cat with crimson whiskers!'

IV

But before he touched the shore,
   The shore of the Bristol Channel,
A sea-green Porpoise carried away
   His wrapper of scarlet flannel.
And when he came to observe his feet
Formerly garnished with toes so neat
His face at once became forlorn
On perceiving that all his toes were gone!

V

And nobody ever knew
   From that dark day to the present,
Whoso had taken the Pobble's toes,
   In a manner so far from pleasant.
Whether the shrimps or crawfish gray,
Or crafty Mermaids stole them away—
Nobody knew; and nobody knows
How the Pobble was robbed of his twice five toes!

VI

The Pobble who has no toes
   Was placed in a friendly Bark,

And they rowed him back, and carried him up,
  To his Aunt Jobiska's Park.
And she made him a feast at his earnest wish
Of eggs and buttercups fried with fish;—
And she said,—'It's a fact the whole world knows,
'That Pobbles are happier without their toes.'

MR. AND MRS. DISCOBBOLOS

I

Mr. and Mrs. Discobbolos
  Climbed to the top of a wall.
 And they sate to watch the sunset sky
 And to hear the Nupiter Piffkin cry
 And the Biscuit Buffalo call.
They took up a roll and some Camomile tea,
And both were as happy as happy could be—
     Till Mrs. Discobbolos said,—
       'Oh! W! X! Y! Z!
       'It has just come into my head—
'Suppose we should happen to fall! ! ! ! !
         'Darling Mr. Discobbolos!

II

'Suppose we should fall down flumpetty
     'Just like pieces of stone!
  'On to the thorns,—or into the moat!
  'What would become of your new green coat?
     'And might you not break a bone?
'It never occurred to me before—
'That perhaps we shall never go down any more!'
     And Mrs. Discobbolos said—
       'Oh! W! X! Y! Z!
       'What put it into your head
'To climb up this wall?—my own
         'Darling Mr. Discobbolos?'
110

Mr. Discobbolos answered,—
    'At first it gave me pain,—
  'And I felt my ears turn perfectly pink
  'When your exclamation made me think
    'We might never get down again!
'But now I believe it is wiser far
'To remain for ever just where we are.'—
    And Mr. Discobbolos said,
      'Oh! W! X! Y! Z!
        'It has just come into my head—
'——We shall never go down again—
          'Dearest Mrs. Discobbolos!'

So Mr. and Mrs. Discobbolos
    Stood up, and began to sing,
  'Far away from hurry and strife
'Here we will pass the rest of life,
    'Ding a dong, ding dong, ding!
'We want no knives nor forks nor chairs,
'No tables nor carpets nor household cares,
      'From worry of life we've fled—
      'Oh! W! X! Y! Z!
      'There is no more trouble ahead,
  'Sorrow or any such thing—
        'For Mr. and Mrs. Discobbolos!'

MR. AND MRS. DISCOBBOLOS

SECOND PART

I

Mr. and Mrs. Discobbolos
   Lived on the top of the wall,
For twenty years, a month and a day,
Till their hair had grown all pearly gray,
   And their teeth began to fall.
They never were ill, or at all dejected,
By all admired, and by some respected,
   Till Mrs. Discobbolos said,
   'O, W! X! Y! Z!
   'It has just come into my head,
'We have have no more room at all—
      'Darling Mr. Discobbolos!

II

'Look at our six fine boys!
   'And our six sweet girls so fair!
'Upon this wall they have all been born,
'And not one of the twelve has happened to fall
   'Through my maternal care!
'Surely they should not pass their lives
'Without any chance of husbands or wives!'
   And Mrs. Discobbolos said,
   'O, W! X! Y! Z!

112

'Did it never come into your head
'That our lives must be lived elsewhere,
      Dearest Mr. Discobbolos?

III

'They have never been at a ball;
  'Nor have even seen a bazaar!
'Nor have heard folks say in a tone all hearty,
"What loves of girls (at a garden party)
  Those Misses Discobbollos are!"
'Morning and night it drives me wild
'To think of the fate of each darling child!'
    But Mr. Discobbolos said,
      'O, W! X! Y! Z!
      'What has come to your fiddledum head!
'What a runcible goose you are!
        'Octopod Mrs. Discobbolos!'

IV

Suddenly Mr. Discobbolos
    Slid from the top of the wall;
  And beneath it he dug a dreadful trench,
  And filled it with dynamite, gunpowder gench,
    And aloud he began to call—
'Let the wild bee sing,
'And the blue bird hum!
'For the end of your lives has certainly come!'
    And Mrs. Discobbolos said,
      'O, W! X! Y! Z!
      'We shall presently all be dead,
'On this ancient runcible wall,
        'Terrible Mr. Discobbolos!'

Pensively, Mr. Discobbolos
   Sat with his back to the wall;
  He lighted a match, and fired the train,
  And the mortified mountain echoed again
   To the sound of an awful fall!
And all the Discobbolos family flew
In thousands of bits to the sky so blue,
   And no one was left to have said,
   'O, W! X! Y! Z!
   'Has it come into anyone's head
  'That the end has happened to all
       'Of the whole of the Clan Discobbolos?'

THE QUANGLE WANGLE'S HAT

I

On the top of the Crumpetty Tree
   The Quangle Wangle sat,
But his face you could not see,
   On account of his Beaver Hat.
For his Hat was a hundred and two feet wide,
With ribbons and bibbons on every side
And bells, and buttons, and loops, and lace;
So that nobody ever could see the face
      Of the Quangle Wangle Quee.

II

The Quangle Wangle said
   To himself on the Crumpetty Tree,—
'Jam; and jelly; and bread;
   'Are the best food for me!

'But the longer I live on this Crumpetty Tree
'The plainer than ever it seems to me
'That very few people come this way
'And that life on the whole is far from gay!'
     Said the Quangle Wangle Quee.

III

But there came to the Crumpetty Tree,
  Mr. and Mrs. Canary;
And they said,—'Did you ever see
  'Any spot so charmingly airy?
'May we build a nest on your lovely Hat?
Mr. Quangle Wangle, grant us that!
'O please let us come and build a nest
'Of whatever material suits you best,
    'Mr. Quangle Wangle Quee!'

IV

And besides, to the Crumpetty Tree
  Came the Stork, the Duck, and the Owl;
The Snail, and the Bumble-Bee,
  The Frog, and the Fimble Fowl;
(The Fimble Fowl, with a Corkscrew leg;)
And all of them said,—We humbly beg,
'We may build our homes on your lovely Hat,—
'Mr. Quangle Wangle, grant us that!
    'Mr. Quangle Wangle Quee!'

V

And the Golden Grouse came there,
  And the Pobble who has no toes,—
And the small Olympian bear,—
  And the Dong with a luminous nose.

And the Blue Baboon, who played the flute,—
And the Orient Calf from the Land of Tute,
And the Attery Squash, and the Bisky Bat,—
All came and built on the lovely Hat
     Of the Quangle Wangle Quee.

VI

And the Quangle Wangle said
    To himself on the Crumpetty Tree,—
'When all these creatures move
    'What a wonderful noise there'll be!'
And at night by the light of the Mulberry moon
They danced to the Flute of the Blue Baboon,
On the broad green leaves of the Crumpetty Tree,
And all were as happy as happy could be,
    With the Quangle Wangle Quee.

MORE LIMERICKS

There was an Old Man of Coblenz,
The length of whose legs was immense;
He went with one prance, from Turkey to France,
That surprising Old Man of Coblenz.

There was an Old Man who said,
'How,—shall I flee from this horrible Cow?
I will sit on this stile, and continue to smile,
Which may soften the heart of that Cow.'

There was a young Lady of Tyre,
Who swept the loud chords of a lyre;
At the sound of each sweep, she enraptured the deep,
And enchanted the city of Tyre.

There was an Old Man of Kamschatka,
Who possessed a remarkably fat cur.
His gait and his waddle, were held as a model,
To all the fat dogs in Kamschatka.

There was an Old Person of Bangor,
Whose face was distorted with anger,
He tore off his boots, and subsisted on roots,
That borascible person of Bangor.

There was an Old Person of Anerley,
Whose conduct was strange and unmannerly;
He rushed down the Strand, with a Pig in each hand,
But returned in the evening to Anerley.

There was an Old Man who said, 'Well!
Will *nobody* answer this bell?
I have pulled day and night, till my hair has grown white,
But nobody answers this bell!'

There was an Old Lady of Prague,
Whose language was horribly vague.
When they said, 'Are these caps?' she answered, 'Perhaps!'
That oracular Lady of Prague.

There was an Old Person of Sparta,
Who had twenty-five sons and one daughter;
He fed them on snails, and weighed them in scales,
That wonderful person of Sparta.

There was an Old Man of Aôsta,
Who possessed a large Cow, but he lost her;
But they said, 'Don't you see, she has rushed up a tree?
You invidious Old Man of Aôsta!'

There was an Old Man of Leghorn,
The smallest as ever was born;
But quickly snapt up he, was once by a puppy,
Who devoured that Old Man of Leghorn.

There was an Old Man, on whose nose,
Most birds of the air could repose;
But they all flew away, at the closing of day,
Which relieved that Old Man and his nose.

NONSENSE ALPHABET II

NONSENSE ALPHABET

A

A was an Area Arch,
　　Where washerwomen sat ;
They made a lot of lovely starch
　　To starch Papa's cravat.

B

B was a Bottle blue,
　　Which was not very small ;
Papa he filled it full of beer,
　　And then he drank it all.

C

C was Papa's gray Cat,
   Who caught a squeaky Mouse;
She pulled him by his twirly tail
   All about the house.

D

D was Papa's white Duck,
   Who had a curly tail;
One day it ate a great fat frog,
   Besides a leetle snail.

E

E was a little Egg,
  Upon the breakfast table;
Papa came in and ate it up,
  As fast as he was able.

F

F was a little Fish.
  Cook in the river took it,
Papa said, 'Cook! Cook! bring a dish!
  And, Cook! be quick and cook it!'

G

G was Papa's new Gun;
   He put it in a box;
And then he went and bought a bun,
   And walked about the Docks.

H

H was Papa's new Hat;
   He wore it on his head;
Outside it was completely black,
   But inside it was red.

I

I was an Inkstand new,
 Papa he likes to use it;
He keeps it in his pocket now,
 For fear that he should lose it.

J

J was some Apple Jam,
 Of which Papa ate part,
But all the rest he took away,
 And stuffed into a tart.

K

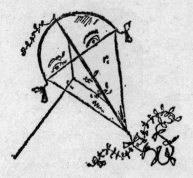

K was a great new Kite;
    Papa he saw it fly
Above a thousand chimney pots,
    And all about the sky.

L

L was a fine new Lamp;
    But when the wick was lit,
Papa he said, 'This light ain't good!
    I cannot read a bit!'

M

M was a dish of Mince;
  It looked so good to eat!
Papa, he quickly ate it up,
  And said, 'This is a treat!'

N

N was a Nut that grew
  High up upon a tree;
Papa, who could not reach it, said,
  'That's *much* too high for me!'

O

O was an Owl who flew
　All in the dark away,
Papa said, 'What an owl you are!
　'Why don't you fly by day?'

P

P was a little Pig,
　Went out to take a walk;
Papa he said, 'If Piggy dead,
　He'd all turn into Pork!'

Q

Q was a Quince that hung
   Upon a garden tree;
Papa he brought it with him home,
   And ate it with his tea.

R

R was a Railway Rug,
   Extremely large and warm;
Papa he wrapped it round his head,
   In a most dreadful storm.

S

S was Papa's new Stick,
  Papa's new thumping Stick,
To thump extremely wicked boys,
  Because it was so thick.

T

T was a Tumbler full
  Of Punch all hot and good;
Papa he drank it up, when in
  The middle of a wood.

U

U was a silver Urn,
  Full of hot scalding water;
Papa said, 'If that Urn were mine,
  I'd give it to my daughter!'

V

V was a Villain; once
  He stole a piece of beef.
Papa he said, 'O! dreadful man!
  That Villain is a Thief!'

W

W was a Watch of Gold:
  It told the time of day,
So that Papa knew when to come,
  And when to go away.

X

X was King Xerxes, whom
  Papa much wished to know;
But this he could not do, because
  Xerxes died long ago.

Y

Y was a Youth, who kicked
  And screamed and cried like mad;
Papa he said, 'Your conduct is
  Abominably bad!'

Z

Z was a Zebra striped
  And streaked with lines of black;
Papa said once, he thought he'd like
  A ride upon his back.

NONSENSE BOTANY

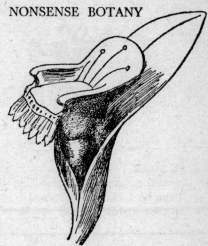

Armchairia Comfortabilis

Bassia Palealensis

Bubblia Blowpipia

Crabbia Horrida

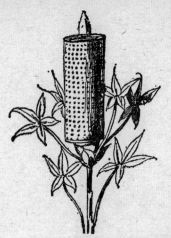

Knutmigrata Simplice

Tureenia Ladlecum

Puffia Leatherbéllowsa

Queeriflora Babyöides

NONSENSE COOKERY

Extract from the *Nonsense Gazette,* for August, 1870.

Our readers will be interested in the following communications from our valued and learned contributor, Professor Bosh, whose labours in the fields of Culinary and Botanical science, are so well known to all the world. The first three Articles richly merit to be added to the Domestic cookery of every family; those which follow, claim the attention of all Botanists, and we are happy to be able through Dr. Bosh's kindness to present our readers with illustrations of his discoveries. All the new flowers are found in the valley of Verrikwier, near the lake of Oddgrow, and on the summit of the hill Orfeltugg.'

THREE RECEIPTS FOR DOMESTIC COOKERY

TO MAKE AN AMBLONGUS PIE

Take 4 pounds (say 4½ pounds) of fresh Amblongusses, and put them in a small pipkin.

Cover them with water and boil them for 8 hours incessantly, after which add 2 pints of new milk, and proceed to boil for 4 hours more.

When you have ascertained that the Amblongusses are quite soft, take them out and place them in a wide pan, taking care to shake them well previously.

Grate some nutmeg over the surface, and cover them carefully with powdered gingerbread, curry-powder, and a sufficient quantity of Cayenne papper.

Remove the pan into the next room, and place it on the floor. Bring it back again, and let it simmer for three-quarters of an hour. Shake the pan violently till all the Amblongusses have become of a pale purple colour.

Then, having prepared the paste, insert the whole carefully, adding at the same time a small pigeon, 2 slices of beef, 4 cauliflowers, and any number of oysters.

Watch patiently till the crust begins to rise, and add a pinch of salt from time to time.

Serve up in a clean dish, and throw the whole out of window as fast as possible.

TO MAKE CRUMBOBBLIOUS CUTLETS

Procure some strips of beef, and having cut them into the smallest possible slices, proceed to cut them still smaller, eight or perhaps nine times.

When the whole is thus minced, brush it up hastily with a new clothes-brush, and stir round rapidly and capriciously with a salt-spoon or a soup-ladle.

Place the whole in a saucepan, and remove it to a sunny place,—say the roof of the house if free from sparrows or other birds,—and leave it there for about a week.

At the end of that time add a little lavender, some oil of almonds, and a few herring-bones; and then cover the whole with 4 gallons of clarified crumbobblious sauce, when it will be ready for use.

Cut it into the shape of ordinary cutlets, and serve up in a clean tablecloth or dinner-napkin.

TO MAKE GOSKY PATTIES

Take a Pig, three or four years of age, and tie him by the off-hind leg to a post. Place 5 pounds of currants, 3 of sugar, 2 pecks of peas, 18 roast chestnuts, a candle, and six bushels of turnips, within his reach; if he eats these, constantly provide him with more.

Then procure some cream, some slices of Cheshire cheese, four quires of foolscap paper, and a packet of black pins. Work the whole into a paste, and spread it out to dry on a sheet of clean brown waterproof linen.

When the paste is perfectly dry, but not before, proceed to beat the Pig violently, with the handle of a large broom. If he squeals, beat him again.

Visit the paste and beat the Pig alternately for some days, and ascertain if at the end of that period the whole is about to turn into Gosky Patties.

If it does not then, it never will; and in that case the Pig may be let loose, and the whole process may be considered as finished.

THE HERALDIC BLAZON OF FOSS THE CAT

['Old Foss', Edward Lear's faithful cat, died at the immense age of seventeen years. Foss predeceased his owner by only a few months, and was buried in the garden of Lear's villa at San Remo.—*Ed.*]

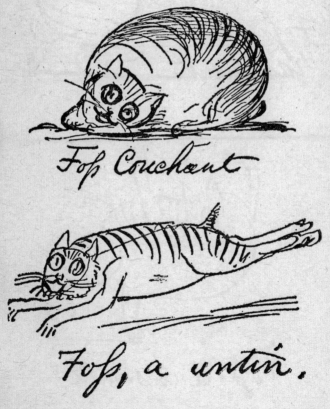

Foſs Couchant

Foſs, a untin.

Fox rampant

Fox dansant

Foss, regardant

Foss Pprpr.

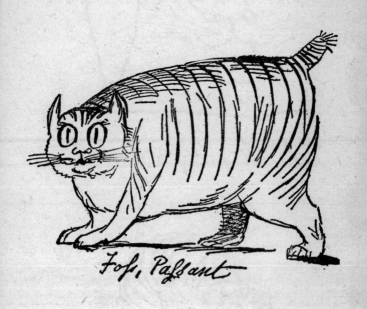

Foß, Paſſant

THE DUCK AND THE KANGAROO
in the autograph of Edward Lear

Said the Duck to the Kangaroo,
  "Good gracious! how you hop!
Over the fields & the water too—
  As if you never would stop!
My life is a bore in this nasty pond
And I long to go out in the world beyond!
  I wish I could hop like you!"
  Said the Duck to the Kangaroo.

"Please give me a ride on your back!"
Said the Duck to the Kangaroo—
I would sit quite still & say nothing but 'Quack'
  The whole of the long day through!
We would go to the Dee, & the Jelly bo lee
All over the land & over the sea,
  Please take me a ride—o do!"
  Said the Duck to the Kangaroo.

Said the Kangaroo to the Duck,—
"It requires a little reflection:—
Perhaps on the whole it may bring me luck,
And there seems but one objection:—
For—(if I'm permitted to speak so bold,)
Your feet are distressingly wet & cold,
And would certainly give me the rheu=
=matiz!" said the Kangaroo.

Said the Duck, "As I sat on the rocks
I thought of all that completely,—
And I bought of pair of worsted socks
Which fit my web-feet neatly.
And to keep out the cold I have bought a cloak
And every day a cigar I'll smoke,
While I follow my own dear true
=Love of a Kangaroo!"—

154

Said the Kangaroo — "I'm ready! "All in the moonlight pale;—
But to balance me well, o my duck! sit steady,
    And quite at the end of my tail!"
So away they went with a hop and a bound,
And they hopped the whole world three times round,
    And who was so happy — o who?
    As the Duck & the Kangaroo.

INCIDENTS IN THE LIFE OF MY UNCLE ARLY

I

O My agèd Uncle Arly!
Sitting on a heap of Barley
    Thro' the silent hours of night,—
Close beside a leafy thicket :—
On his nose there was a Cricket,—
In his hat a Railway-Ticket;—
    (But his shoes were far too tight.)

II

Long ago, in youth, he squander'd
All his goods away, and wander'd
    To the Tiniskoop-hills afar.
There on golden sunsets blazing,
Every evening found him gazing,—
Singing,—'Orb! you're quite amazing!
    'How I wonder what you are!'

III

Like the ancient Medes and Persians,
Always by his own exertions
    He subsisted on those hills ;—

Whiles,—by teaching children spelling,—
Or at times by merely yelling,—
Or at intervals by selling
    Propter's Nicodemus Pills.'

IV

Later, in his morning rambles
He perceived the moving brambles—
    Something square and white disclose;—
'Twas a First-class Railway-Ticket;
But, on stooping down to pick it
Off the ground,—a pea-green Cricket
    Settled on my uncle's Nose.

V

Never—never more,—oh! never,
Did that Cricket leave him ever,—
    Dawn or evening, day or night;—
Clinging as a constant treasure,—
Chirping with a cheerious measure,—
Wholly to my uncle's pleasure,—
    (Though his shoes were far too tight.)

VI

So for three-and-forty winters,
Till his shoes were worn to splinters,
    All those hills he wander'd o'er,—
Sometimes silent;—sometimes yelling;—
Till he came to Borley-Melling,
Near his old ancestral dwelling;—
    (But his shoes were far too tight.)

VII

On a little heap of Barley
Died my agèd uncle Arly,
    And they buried him one night;—
Close beside the leafy thicket;—
There,—his hat and Railway-Ticket;—
There,—his ever-faithful Cricket;—
(But his shoes were far too tight.)

THE END

FURTHER ICON BOOKS

MARRIED TO TOLSTOY (B7)

Cynthia Asquith   **7s. 6d.**

Illustrated

Cynthia Asquith's book is neither hostile to Tolstoy nor biased. She is concerned to tell the *whole* story. . .

"One of the most astonishing exposures ever made of the sheer agony of being married to a genius."

Beverley Nichols, *Woman's Own*

All enquiries about the Icon series of paperbacks should be addressed to:
The Editor, Icon Books, Ltd., 9 Down Street, London, W.1

FURTHER ICON BOOKS

AYESHA: The Return of She (F14)

H. Rider Haggard   **5s.**

"... this lost soul who refuses to die until her beloved returns to earth again, occupies a position—at least, in my mind—comparable to the Sun in the galaxy of immortal lovers."

Henry Miller,
"The Books in My Life"

All enquiries about the Icon series of paperbacks should be addressed to:
The Editor, Icon Books, Ltd., 9 Down Street, London, W.1